Hi, everyone! It's your pal Eleanor! My friends and I are going shopping in a big toy store. Do you want to go, too? Come on! We'd love to have you!

See these stars? Each time you learn something new, you get one of these stickers. When you finish a whole section, you will get a big train car sticker to add to your Certificate of Completion at the end of this book.

One more thing! When you see this picture of me and my book, it means I am there to give you a little help! Just look for **Eleanor's Tips**.

Eleanor's Tips

When you match letters, look carefully! Some letters look almost the same.

B D   E F

Pierre likes toys that go *vroom!* **Help him put all the drivers in their seats. Draw a line from the letter on each driver to the matching letter on the toy.**

·Help me set the table for a tea party.
Circle the letter on each plate that matches the letter on the teacup beside it.

A B C D E F G H I J K L M N O P Q R S T U V W X Y Z

"Play ball!" yells Casey. You and Casey can play a special ball game.

Draw a line connecting the letters that match.

A B C D E F G H I J K L M N O P Q R S T U V W X Y Z

Kisha has found the art supplies! She likes what she sees in her drawing. What do you see?
Draw lines connecting the matching letters.

A B C D E F G H I J K L M N O P Q R S T U V W X Y Z

Chug-chug! Choo-choo! I like to play with trains.
Draw a line connecting the letters that match.

A B C D E F G H I J K L M N O P Q R S T U V W X Y Z

Casey needs your help to find the letters.
Color the letters on the computer keyboard that match the ones on the screen. Draw lines to connect them.

A B C D E F G H I J K L M N O P Q R S T U V W X Y Z

C   Q
  D
S   G

Q W E R T Y U I O P
A S D F G H J K L M
Z X C   N B V

Great job! Put your star sticker here.
Now jump ahead to the next page.

Alphabet Identification   7

Eleanor's Tips

If you're not sure how to write a letter, **trace** it first. Then write the letter.

Help Kisha put each baby animal with its mother.

Look at the letter on each baby's shirt. Then trace the same letter on her mother's shirt.

Pierre loves making music. Help him put the instruments back in their cases.

Look at the first letter of each instrument. Then write the same letter on the line next to its matching case.

Let's play an alphabet game.

**Follow the path from START to FINISH.
Say the name of the letter in each space.
Color each space a different color. Once
you're at the finish line, you know all the
letters of the alphabet!**

START

K
J
I
H
M
N
F
G
E
D
C
B
A

cellent! Place a train car sticker on your Certificate of
mpletion. Then jump ahead for more fun with alphabet puzzles.

Eleanor's Tips

A **maze** is a tricky path on which it's easy to get lost! You can find your way through mazes by looking carefully.

This robot will move if I find all the R's.

Draw a line that follows the trail of R's through the maze from START to FINISH.

START

FINISH

Pierre and Kisha are playing in their alphabet house.

Help them explore the house from A to Z! Color the trail of the alphabet.

START

FINISH

Good job! Place your star sticker here.
Now jump ahead to the next page.

In a **word search**, look **across** each row. Then look **down** each column.

What a funny monster puppet show! The big monster is teaching the little monster the ABC's.

Draw a circle around the letters A, B, and C each time you see them in the puzzle.

A	B	C	D
B	P	S	A
C	S	T	B
E	A	B	C

I'm pretending to be a doctor. I must help my friend Kisha get well.

Put a circle around the letters O and K each time you see them together in the puzzle.

O	O	K	I
C	K	J	O
O	D	O	K
K	C	M	H

Say O and K out loud, and you will hear how Kisha feels.

Putting letters in a special order makes words or names— such as Kisha!

Kisha has made a necklace with her name on it. Can you find Kisha's name three times on the board?

Circle the letters that spell K-I-S-H-A.

O K I S H A O C D
O C D Q Q D O C O
C D Q K I S H A Q
O C O Q C Q D C D
D C D O D Q C O Q
O K I S H A Q D C

Star Stickers

Ticket

Level 1 stars

Level 2 stars

Level 3 stars

Certificate Reward Stickers

train car 1   train car 2   train car 3

Extra JumpStart Stickers

venture. Sticker ISBN 0-439-18537-8 Wrkbk ISBN 0-439-17650-6

Pierre hopes his gumball will have the letter X on it.
Find and color all the gumballs with the letter X.

How many **X**'s did you find?

Great job! Place your star sticker here.
Now jump ahead to the next page.

Eleanor's Tips

The **order** of letters in a word is important. **N** and **O** spell **NO**. **O** and **N** spell **ON**.

Help Casey spell his name with these alphabet blocks.

Trace the line from each block to the top of Casey's tower. Write that letter on the empty block.

Help me put my blocks in ABC order starting with **A**.

Write these alphabet letters in order on the empty blocks. Singing the ABC song will help.

Excellent job! Place your star sticker here.
Now jump ahead to see what you've learned.

Alphabet Puzzles ⟨**19**⟩

Play a letter game with Kisha and Casey.

Follow the line from each letter on the castle wall to the space where that letter goes.

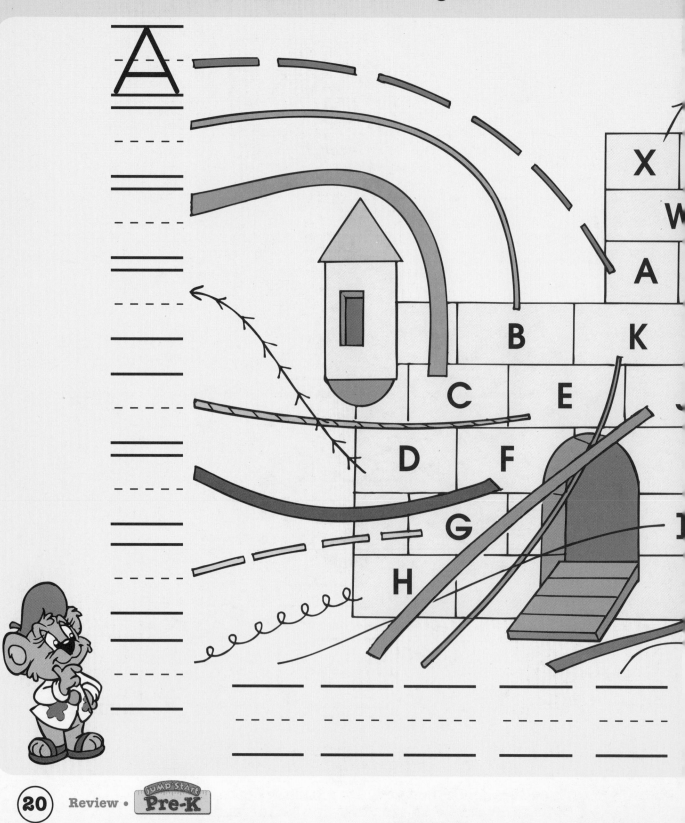

Write the letter in the empty space. Then read all the letters of the alphabet from A to Z. Can you sing the alphabet song as you look at the letters you wrote?

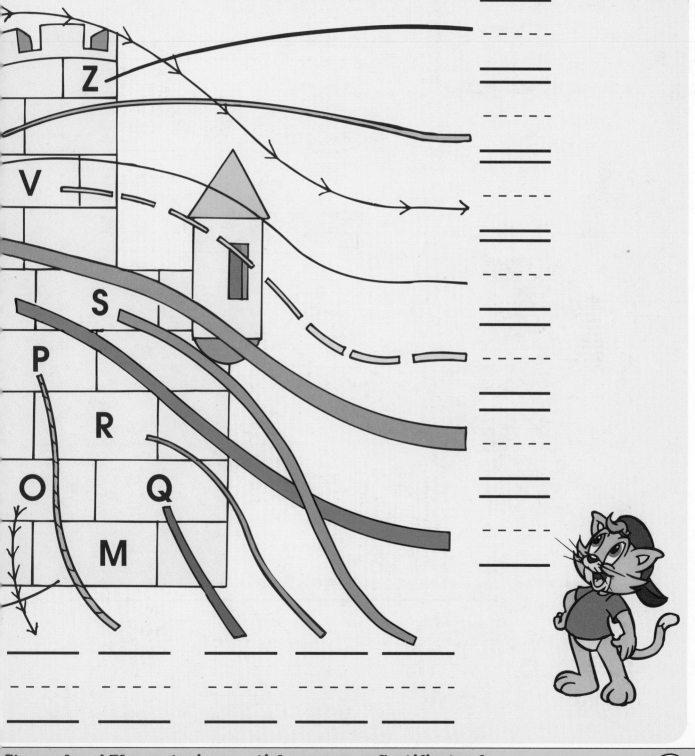

Stupendous! Place a train car sticker on your Certificate of Completion. Now jump ahead for fun with beginning sounds.

Review **21**

Eleanor's Tips

Say words out loud to hear their beginning sound!

Help me find my favorite toys. They all have the same beginning sound as **b**alloon and **b**utterfly. **Circle each one.**

Help Pierre make a toy zoo!

Look at each group of animals. Say each animal's name out loud. Then draw a line to connect the animals in each group that have the same beginning sound.

Good job! Place your star sticker here. Now jump ahead to the next page.

Beginning Sounds **23**

Eleanor's Tips

Words with the same beginning sound usually start with the same letter!

bat   **b**ook   **b**all

Kisha has found a toy that has the same beginning sound as her name!

Circle the things on each shelf that have the same beginning sound as each letter card.

L

G

J

W

I know what this toy rabbit wants—a ride in the rocket!

Draw a line from the letter R to each thing with the same beginning sound as rocket.

Help Pierre deliver a package to the pig's palace.
Follow the path of **P**'s and the pictures with the same beginning sound as package.

START

FINISH

Casey needs your help to play this computer game.
Say each picture name. Then circle the letter that makes that beginning sound.

S L

T D

B R

J P

K M

H B

Great job! Place your star sticker here.
Now jump ahead to the next page.

Beginning Sounds 27

I like to play teacher. Can you help Pierre choose the letter with the same beginning sound as each picture?

Write it on the line.

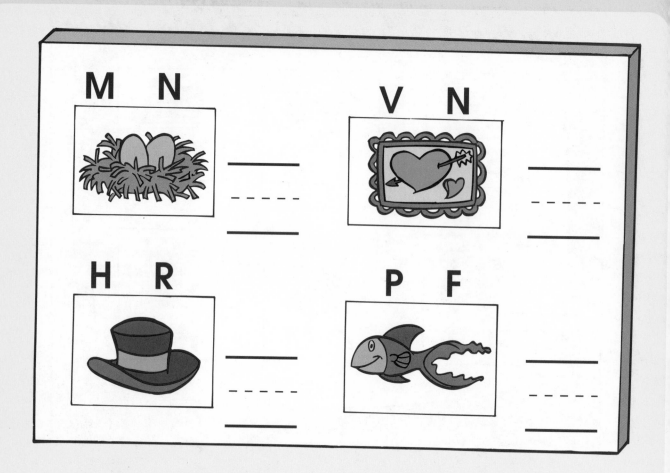

Casey needs your help to play this computer game.
Say each picture name. Then circle the letter that makes that beginning sound.

S L

T D

B R

J P

K M

H B

**Great job! Place your star sticker here.
Now jump ahead to the next page.**

I like to play teacher. Can you help Pierre choose the letter with the same beginning sound as each picture?

Write it on the line.

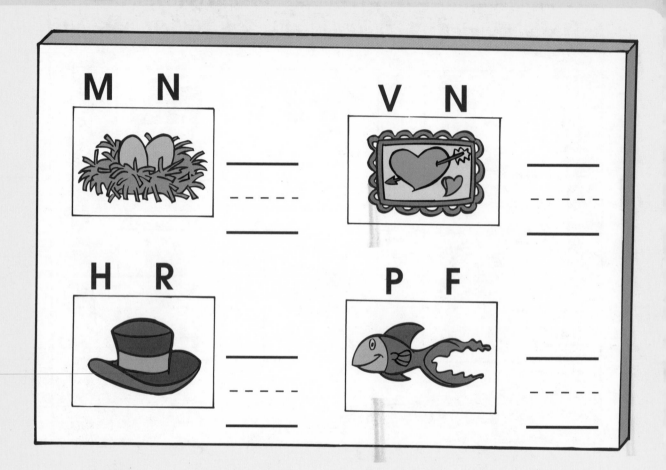

M N

V N

H R

P F

Help Casey decide where to put away the toys.
Write the letter that makes the beginning sound of all the toys on the shelf. Then draw a line from each of Casey's toys to the right shelf.

Excellent! Place your star sticker here.
Now jump ahead to see what you've learned.

Beginning Sounds   29

It's time to go home! Help each of us find our way out of the toy store. Each of us will take a different path.

Start with Kisha. If you pass a letter, say a word that starts with that letter. If you go past a toy on the path, say the letter that picture name starts with. Draw a line through each path as you go.

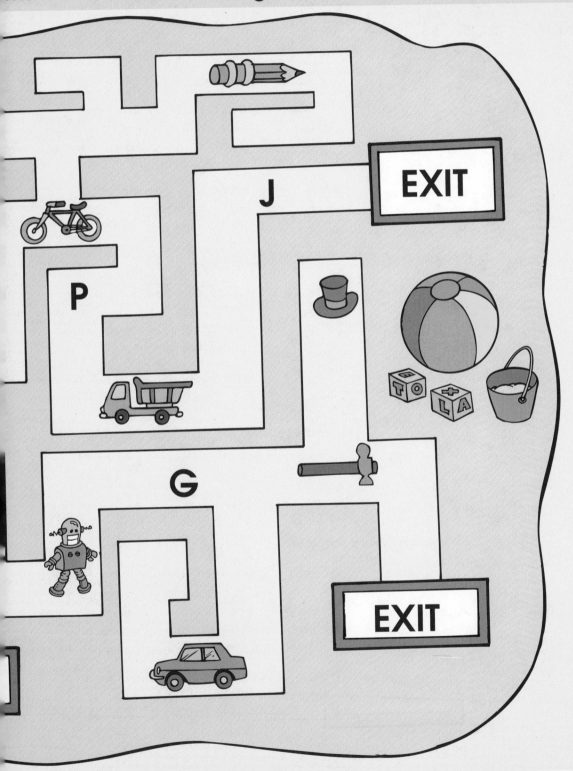

You did it! Place your last train car sticker on your Certificate of Completion. Great job!

Review 31

Answer Key

PAGE 2	draw lines to connect matching letters
PAGE 3	circle G, R, F, I, K, J
PAGE 4	draw lines to connect matching letters
PAGE 5	draw lines to connect matching letters
PAGE 6	draw lines to connect matching letters
PAGE 7	color C, D, G, Q, S keys on keyboard; draw lines to connect letters to screen
PAGE 8	trace A, F, C, Z
PAGE 9	write D, V, G, X
PAGES 10–11	color alphabet path A to Z
PAGE 12	draw path line that connects the R's
PAGE 13	color alphabet path from A to Z
PAGE 14	circle three A's, four B's, three C's
PAGE 15	circle five OK's
PAGE 16	circle "Kisha" three times
PAGE 17	color five X gumballs
PAGE 18	write C, A, S, E, Y
PAGE 19	write A, B, C, D, E
PAGES 20–21	write alphabet letters A to Z
PAGE 22	circle blocks, beach ball, balloon, boat, butterfly, baseball, binoculars, bat, bicycle, bottle
PAGE 23	draw lines to connect monkey/mouse, turtle/turkey, snail/snake, cow/cat, dog/dinosaur, fish/frog
PAGE 24	circle lion/lamp, guitar/gorilla, jump rope/jack-in-the-box, whistle/watch
PAGE 25	draw lines from R to ring, ruler, rocking chair, rainbow, rocks
PAGE 26	follow maze line through path of P's and pear, pot, peas, puppet, pumpkin, paint, pencil, panda
PAGE 27	circle S, D, R, J, K, B
PAGE 28	write N, V, H, F
PAGE 29	write S, F, T, B; draw lines to connect train/second shelf from bottom, bells/bottom shelf, fan/third shelf from bottom, shoe/top shelf
PAGES 30–31	draw lines through the maze from each character to the exit signs; answers will vary